PHONICS
Reading Program

BIKINI BOTTOM ADVENTURES

by Sonia Sander

SCHOLASTIC INC.

New York   Toronto   London   Auckland   Sydney
Mexico City   New Delhi   Hong Kong   Buenos Aires

Patrick at the Krusty Krab, ISBN 0-439-77957-X, Copyright © 2005 by Viacom International Inc.
In a Fix, ISBN 0-439-77962-6, Copyright © 2005 by Viacom International Inc.
Stopped Clock, ISBN 0-439-77966-9, Copyright © 2005 by Viacom International Inc.
Rub-A-Dub-Dub, ISBN 0-439-77967-7, Copyright © 2005 by Viacom International Inc.
Tell Me, Magic Shell, ISBN 0-439-77968-5, Copyright © 2005 by Viacom International Inc.
Hide and Sneak, ISBN 0-439-77969-3, Copyright © 2005 by Viacom International Inc.
Lunch Rush, ISBN 0-439-77970-7, Copyright © 2005 by Viacom International Inc.
Bubble Busters, ISBN 0-439-77971-5, Copyright © 2005 by Viacom International Inc.
SpongeBob Saves the Day, ISBN 0-439-77972-3, Copyright © 2005 by Viacom International Inc.
Ice Cream Time, ISBN 0-439-77973-1, Copyright © 2005 by Viacom International Inc.
Mussel Beach, ISBN 0-439-77974-X, Copyright © 2005 by Viacom International Inc.
Boat Trouble, ISBN 0-439-77975-8, Copyright © 2005 by Viacom International Inc.

ISNB-13: 978-0-545-01373-4
ISBN-10: 0-545-01373-9

Stephen Hillenburg

Based on the TV series SpongeBob SquarePants® created by
Stephen Hillenburg as seen on Nickelodeon®

Used under license by Scholastic Inc. Published by Scholastic Inc.
SCHOLASTIC and associated logos are trademarks and/or
registered trademarks of Scholastic Inc.

12 11 10 9 8 7 6 5 4 3 2 1   7 8 9 10 11/0

Printed in Singapore
First compilation printing, June 2007

Welcome to **SpongeBob SquarePants'** Phonics Reading Program!

Learning to read is so important for your child's success in school and in life. Now your child can learn important phonics skills with the help of **SpongeBob SquarePants**. Here's the BIG idea about how these stories work:

Take phonics, the fundamental skill of knowing that the sounds we say represent the letters we read. Add **SpongeBob** and help your child LEARN and LOVE to read!

Scholastic has been helping families encourage young readers for more than 80 years. These books are based on the best research on how children develop reading skills. To be a good reader, it takes practice. That's where **SpongeBob SquarePants** can make a difference. Kids love **SpongeBob** and will want to read his latest adventures over and over again. Try these ideas for enjoying the books with your child:

 Read together by taking turns line by line or page by page.

 Look for more words that have the same sounds as the words in the reader.

 Have your child read the story to you and then retell it in his or her own words.

Thank you for letting us help you support your beginning reader.

Happy reading,

Francie Alexander,
Chief Academic Officer, Scholastic Inc.

PHONICS
Reading Program

• Table of Contents •

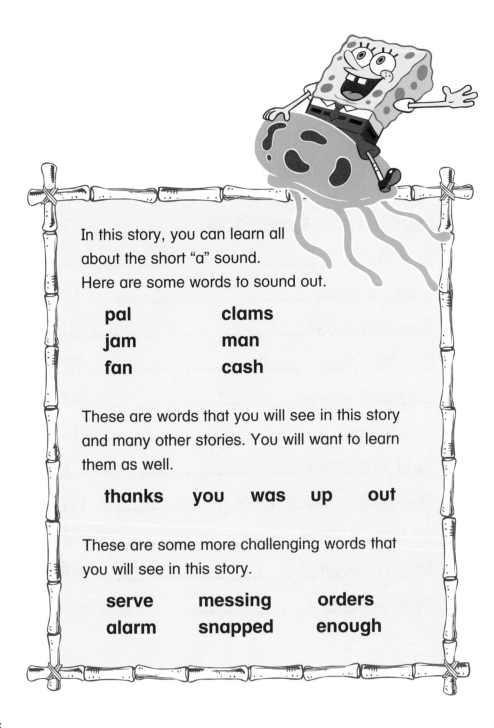

In this story, you can learn all about the short "a" sound.
Here are some words to sound out.

pal	clams
jam	man
fan	cash

These are words that you will see in this story and many other stories. You will want to learn them as well.

thanks **you** **was** **up** **out**

These are some more challenging words that you will see in this story.

serve	messing	orders
alarm	snapped	enough

PATRICK AT THE KRUSTY KRAB

by Sonia Sander

"I am sorry you are
feeling bad, SpongeBob,"
said Patrick.
"Hey, I can work at the Krusty
Krab for you!"
"Thanks, Patrick," said
SpongeBob.
"You are a pal."

"SpongeBob called in sick
today," said Mr. Krabs.
"Oh, please," said Squidward.
"I can't cook and serve."
"You don't have to!"
said Patrick.
"I will make the Krabby Patties
today."

Patrick kept messing
up the orders.
"That was jellyfish jelly
on the clams, not kelp jam,"
said Squidward.

"Oh, man!" called Squidward.
"Sound the alarm and turn on
the fan!
The Krabby Patties are
on fire."

Mr. Krabs was a bit mad.
"Patrick, my lad," he snapped.
"If you make me lose cash,
I'll break out in a rash!"

There was a loud crash!
"Aaah!" cried Patrick as
he ran into some cans.
"That's it!" said Squidward.
"I've had enough! I can stack
them up myself."

Patrick sat down
and took a nap.
"Do not wake him,"
said Mr. Krabs.
"Patrick napping is the
best help he can give!"

"Glad to see you back, SpongeBob!" said Mr. Krabs. Even Squidward agreed.

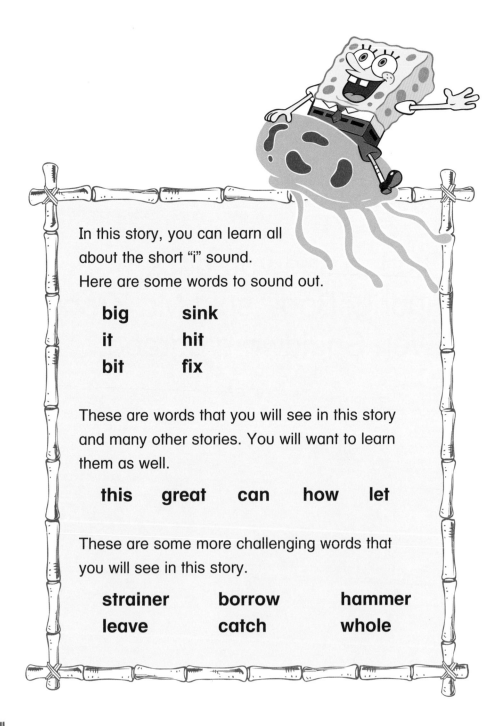

In this story, you can learn all
about the short "i" sound.
Here are some words to sound out.

big	**sink**
it	**hit**
bit	**fix**

These are words that you will see in this story
and many other stories. You will want to learn
them as well.

this **great** **can** **how** **let**

These are some more challenging words that
you will see in this story.

strainer	**borrow**	**hammer**
leave	**catch**	**whole**

IN A FIX

by Sonia Sander

"What is this big thing
in your sink?" asked
SpongeBob.
"It is a strainer," said
Squidward.
"Feel free to borrow it
and leave."

"This is great for jellyfishing!" said Patrick.

"It was nice of Squidward to let us use it," said SpongeBob.

Patrick slipped,
then tripped.
He missed the jellyfish
and hit the ground.

"Hopping clams! It ripped a bit!" said SpongeBob.
"How can we fix it?" asked Patrick.

"We will fix it with
a hammer," said
SpongeBob.
"We will hit it just
like this."

"We did not catch any
jellyfish, but it was nice
of you to let us use this,"
Patrick told Squidward.

"How did you fix it?"
  asked Squidward.
"I gave it to you broken."
"Oh, it was no big deal,"
  said SpongeBob.
"We are good at fixing
  things."

"Hey, Squidward," cried SpongeBob. "We will fix up your whole house if you want!"

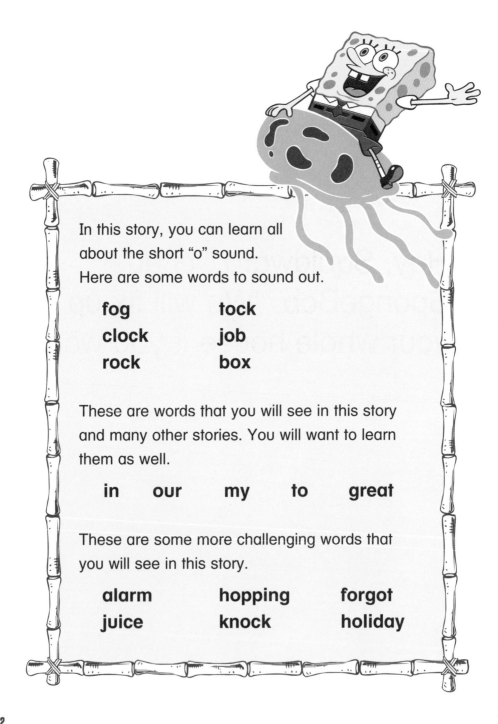

In this story, you can learn all
about the short "o" sound.
Here are some words to sound out.

fog	**tock**
clock	**job**
rock	**box**

These are words that you will see in this story
and many other stories. You will want to learn
them as well.

in　　**our**　　**my**　　**to**　　**great**

These are some more challenging words that
you will see in this story.

alarm	**hopping**	**forgot**
juice	**knock**	**holiday**

STOPPED CLOCK

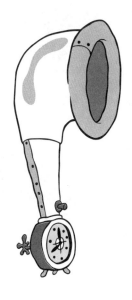

by Sonia Sander

Tick-tock.

Tick-tock.

SpongeBob's fog
alarm clock stopped.

"Oh, no!" cried
  SpongeBob.
"My clock stopped!
  I am late for my job!"

"Hopping clams!"
cried SpongeBob.
"I tripped on my pet
rock and dropped
my juice box!"

"Oh, tartar sauce!"
cried SpongeBob.
"My mop is tied in
a knot!"

"Oh, barnacles!"
cried SpongeBob.
"I forgot to lock my
front door!"

Knock, knock.
"Squidward!" cried
SpongeBob.
"Get up! We are late
for our jobs!"

"It is a holiday,
   SpongeBob,"
   said Squidward.
"The Krusty Krab
   is closed."

"Holidays are great for not setting the alarm clock," said SpongeBob.

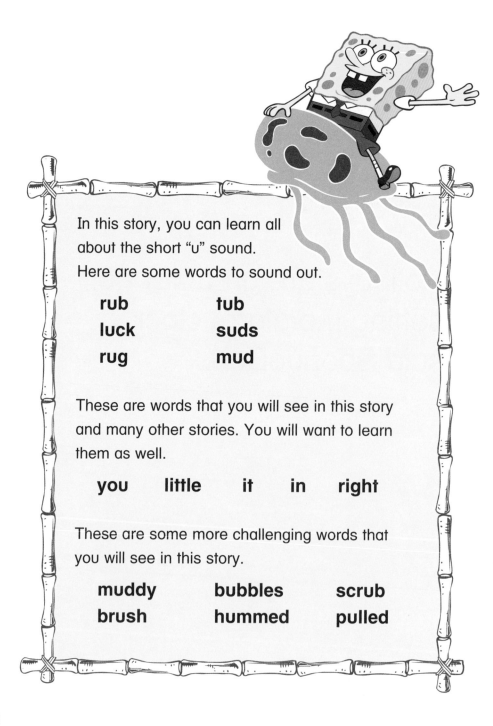

In this story, you can learn all about the short "u" sound.
Here are some words to sound out.

rub	**tub**
luck	**suds**
rug	**mud**

These are words that you will see in this story and many other stories. You will want to learn them as well.

you   **little**   **it**   **in**   **right**

These are some more challenging words that you will see in this story.

muddy	**bubbles**	**scrub**
brush	**hummed**	**pulled**

RUB-A-DUB-DUB

by Sonia Sander

"Look what I got you,"
 said SpongeBob.

"Just my luck,"
 said Squidward.
"A muddy rug."

"I know,"
said SpongeBob.
"We can put it
in the tub."

"You put in too much soap,"
said Squidward.
"You made too many
suds in the tub."
"But the bubbles
are so much fun!"
said SpongeBob.

"This scrub brush
will rub the mud
right off the rug,"
said SpongeBob.

SpongeBob hummed
as he scrubbed the rug.
Squidward plugged his ears.
"Can we lower the volume,
please?" yelled Squidward.

They pulled the rug
out of the tub.
"The mud is gone,"
said Squidward.
"But you made a hole."
"We can just cut the rug,"
said SpongeBob.

"It is such a nice little rug," said SpongeBob.

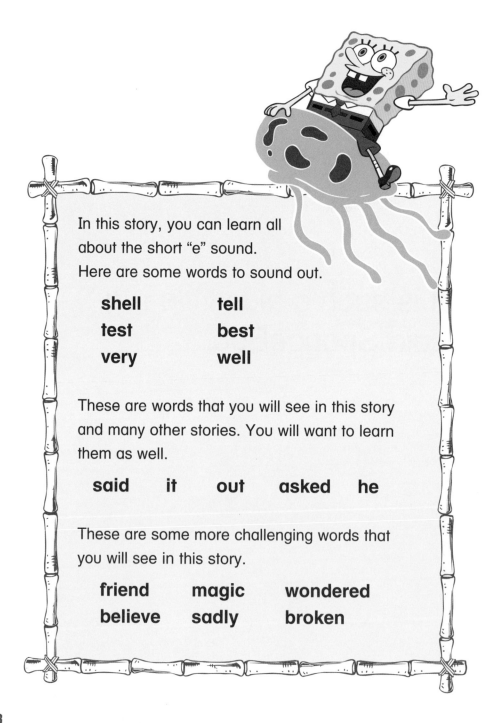

In this story, you can learn all
about the short "e" sound.
Here are some words to sound out.

shell	**tell**
test	**best**
very	**well**

These are words that you will see in this story
and many other stories. You will want to learn
them as well.

said   **it**   **out**   **asked**   **he**

These are some more challenging words that
you will see in this story.

friend	**magic**	**wondered**
believe	**sadly**	**broken**

NICKELODEON™

SpongeBob SquarePants™

Phonics Reading Program

Book 5 · short e

TELL ME, MAGIC SHELL

by Sonia Sander

"Look, Patrick,"
said SpongeBob.
"It is the magic shell.
Let's test it out."

"Tell me, magic shell,"
 said SpongeBob.
"Is Patrick my
 very best friend?"
"Ask next time,"
 said the magic shell.

"Is it next time?"
Patrick wondered.
"Yes," said SpongeBob
as he pulled the cord again.
"Oh, magic shell,
is my best friend pink?"

They bent down
to hear what the
shell had to say.
"No," said the shell.

SpongeBob and Patrick
could not believe it.
"I am not your best friend?"
asked Patrick sadly.
"Who is, then?"

"Well, I think you are,"
said SpongeBob.
"Then the shell
must be broken!"
said Patrick.
"You have been my
best friend since the
day we met."

"Aw, Patrick,"
said SpongeBob.
"No silly magic shell
can tell us if we are friends."
"But let's ask it one more
time just for fun," said Patrick.
The shell said, "Yes."

"It's right!" yelled Patrick. "All you have to do is ask many times. Now that's magic!"

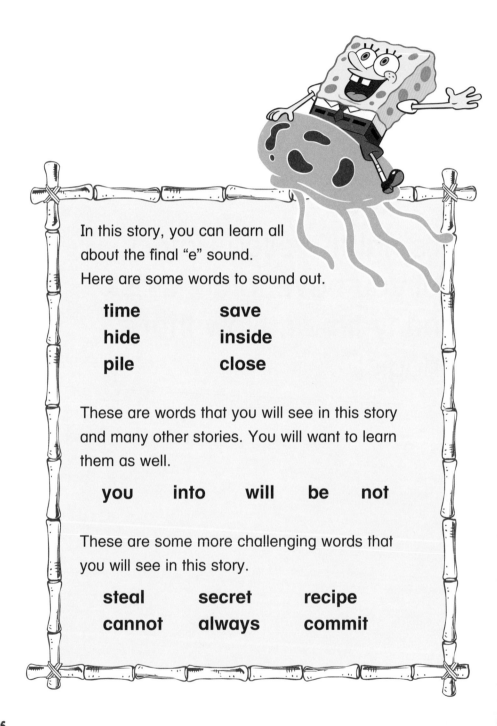

In this story, you can learn all about the final "e" sound.
Here are some words to sound out.

time	**save**
hide	**inside**
pile	**close**

These are words that you will see in this story and many other stories. You will want to learn them as well.

you   **into**   **will**   **be**   **not**

These are some more challenging words that you will see in this story.

steal	**secret**	**recipe**
cannot	**always**	**commit**

HIDE AND SNEAK

by Sonia Sander

I love Krabby Patties!
So does Plankton.
He wants to steal
the recipe.

But I will stop
him every time.
I will save the
secret recipe.

Nice try, Plankton.
You cannot hide
on the other side
of this pile of cans.
I will not let you
swipe the recipe.

If you dare to spy inside
the Krusty Krab,
you will be mine.
You will not dine long.
You will not bite into
a Krabby Patty.

Wise up, Plankton.
I am always close by.
I will see you steal a
bite of Krabby Patty
from that plate.

If you take that bite
back to your place
to study it, I will
follow you. I will take
that bite back.

Face it, Plankton,
you have no hope.
You may as well
give up.
I will not let you
commit a crime.

The secret recipe
is safe with me here.

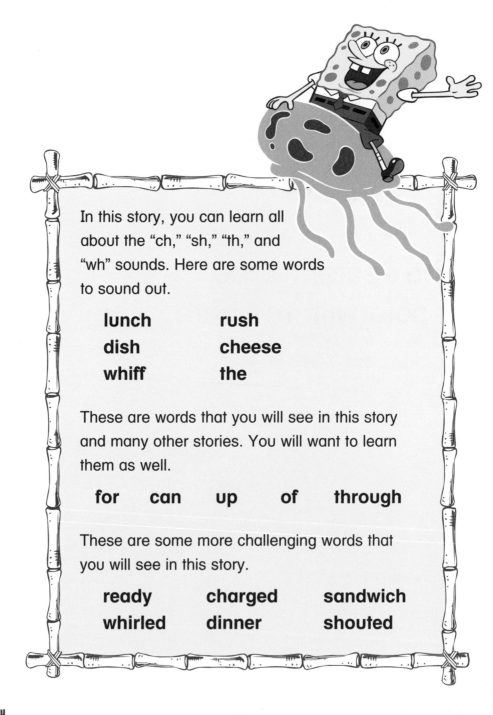

In this story, you can learn all about the "ch," "sh," "th," and "wh" sounds. Here are some words to sound out.

lunch	**rush**
dish	**cheese**
whiff	**the**

These are words that you will see in this story and many other stories. You will want to learn them as well.

for **can** **up** **of** **through**

These are some more challenging words that you will see in this story.

ready	**charged**	**sandwich**
whirled	**dinner**	**shouted**

LUNCH RUSH

by Sonia Sander

"Ready for the
lunch rush?"
shouted SpongeBob.
"I can hardly wait,"
said Squidward.

The lunch crowd charged
through the doors.
The Krusty Krab was packed.

SpongeBob chopped the chilled lettuce and prepared the cheese for the patties.

A whiff of Krabby Patties whirled through the air. Squidward served up dish after dish.

SpongeBob was so
busy he forgot to
add the fresh
Krabby Patties!

Whoops!
SpongeBob cooked up
a Cheesy Patty
instead of a
Krabby Patty!

Crunch, crunch.
Munch, munch.
The cheesy sandwich
came flying back.

"Let's get ready for the dinner rush!" said SpongeBob.

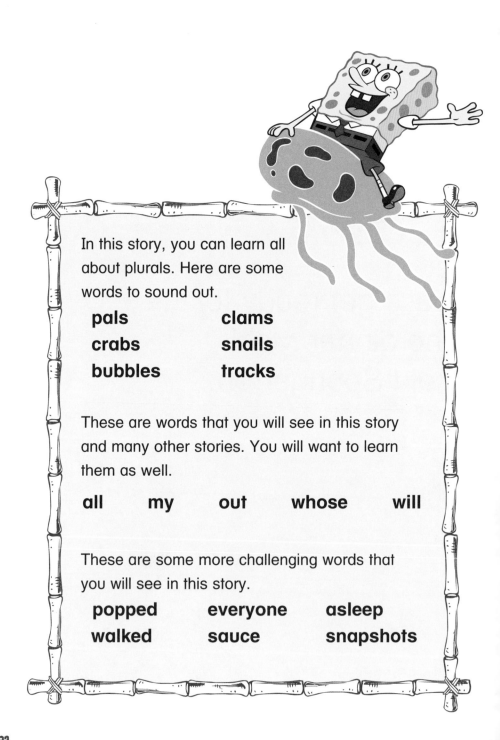

In this story, you can learn all about plurals. Here are some words to sound out.

pals	**clams**
crabs	**snails**
bubbles	**tracks**

These are words that you will see in this story and many other stories. You will want to learn them as well.

all   **my**   **out**   **whose**   **will**

These are some more challenging words that you will see in this story.

popped	**everyone**	**asleep**
walked	**sauce**	**snapshots**

BUBBLE BUSTERS

by Sonia Sander

"Sleep well, my
   bubble pals,"
   said SpongeBob.
"I will make more
   pals for you when
   I wake up."

"Hopping clams," cried SpongeBob. "Where are all of my crabs, snails, and clams?"

"I need to find out where
my bubble pals went,"
said SpongeBob.
"I will look for clues.
Whose footprints are
these?"

The tracks led next door.
"Those are your tracks,
SpongeBob,"
said Squidward.

SpongeBob asked
Squidward and
Patrick for help.
"I will help if you leave me
  alone," said Squidward.
"I will help for free!" said
  Patrick.

Everyone sat in their chairs.
The stars came out.
Zzzzzzzz.
SpongeBob and Patrick
fell asleep.

SpongeBob got up
and walked in his sleep.
He popped all of the bubbles!
Squidward took snapshots.

"Oh, tartar sauce!"
cried SpongeBob.
"It was me all along!"

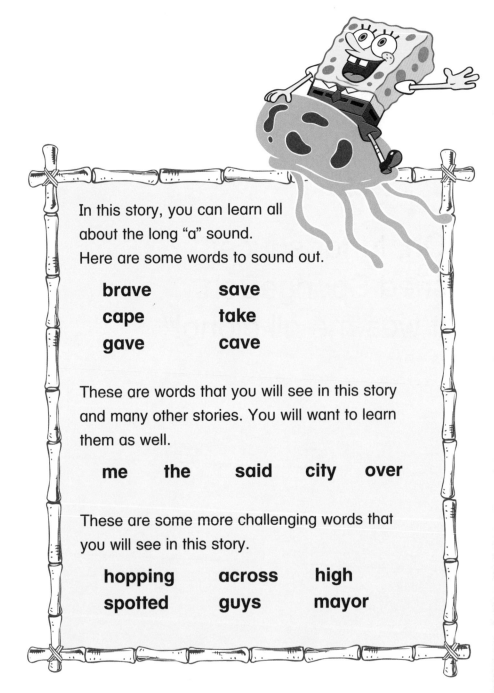

In this story, you can learn all about the long "a" sound. Here are some words to sound out.

brave	**save**
cape	**take**
gave	**cave**

These are words that you will see in this story and many other stories. You will want to learn them as well.

me **the** **said** **city** **over**

These are some more challenging words that you will see in this story.

hopping	**across**	**high**
spotted	**guys**	**mayor**

Phonics Reading Program
Book 9 · long a

SPONGEBOB SAVES THE DAY

by Sonia Sander

"Hopping clams!"
 cried SpongeBob.
"Gary is gone!"

"I must be brave and go save Gary!" said SpongeBob as he put on his cape.

SpongeBob took off
to find Gary.
He raced across the sky.
He looked high and low.

SpongeBob spotted
some bad guys and
followed them to a cave.
"Meow," said Gary.

SpongeBob chased the bad guys. He saved Gary. SpongeBob gave the bad guys over to the cops.

"I am glad you are
safe, Gary,"
said SpongeBob.
"I'll never let anyone
take you away again."

"For capturing those criminals and making
Bikini Bottom safe again, please take this key to
the city," said the mayor.

SpongeBob woke from his dream.

"Aw, Gary, you are always safe with me," he said.

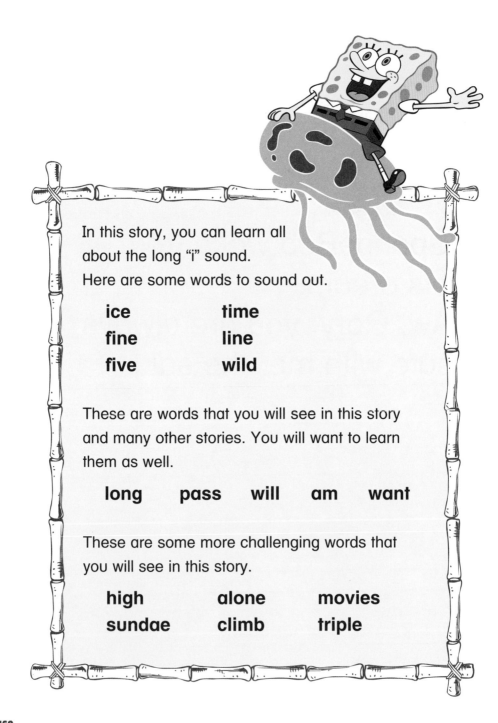

In this story, you can learn all about the long "i" sound.
Here are some words to sound out.

ice	**time**
fine	**line**
five	**wild**

These are words that you will see in this story and many other stories. You will want to learn them as well.

long   **pass**   **will**   **am**   **want**

These are some more challenging words that you will see in this story.

high	**alone**	**movies**
sundae	**climb**	**triple**

NICKELODEON™

SpongeBob SquarePants™

Phonics Reading Program
Book 10 · long i

ICE CREAM TIME

by Sonia Sander

"Hey, buddy,"
yelled SpongeBob.
"It is ice cream time!"

"The line is long
  but I don't mind,"
  said Patrick.
"Hey!" said SpongeBob.
"Let's play *I Spy* to pass
  the time!"

"I spy Squidward!"
said Patrick.
"We will stand
in line with you,"
said SpongeBob.
"No, I am fine,"
said Squidward.

"Let's spin five times,"
 said Patrick.
"Do you mind?"
 asked Squidward.
"I find your spins too wild!"

"Climb up to see
how long the line is,"
said SpongeBob.
"It is one mile long,"
said Patrick.

"I want a triple sky-high
ice cream sundae!"
said SpongeBob.
"And I want mine to be
this wide," said Patrick.

"I like to eat
  mine all alone,"
  said Squidward.
"You two can slide in
  right over there."
"You are too kind,"
  said SpongeBob.

"I liked eating ice cream with you," said SpongeBob.

"Me, too," said Patrick.

"Now let's go wait in line at the movies!"

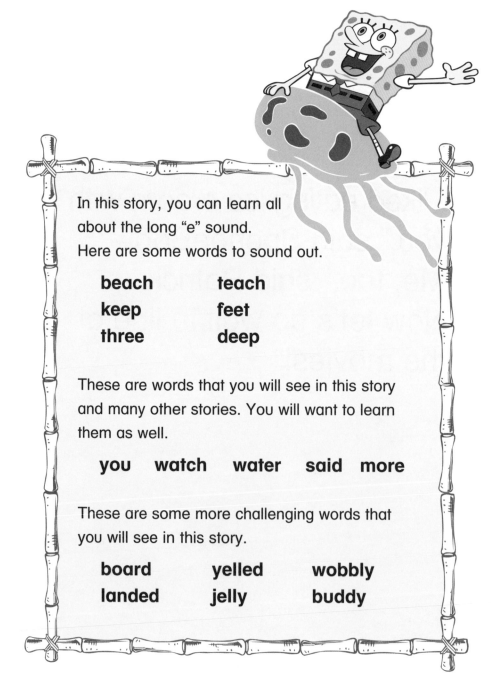

In this story, you can learn all about the long "e" sound.
Here are some words to sound out.

beach	**teach**
keep	**feet**
three	**deep**

These are words that you will see in this story and many other stories. You will want to learn them as well.

you   watch   water   said   more

These are some more challenging words that you will see in this story.

board	**yelled**	**wobbly**
landed	**jelly**	**buddy**

MUSSEL BEACH

by Sonia Sander

SpongeBob and Patrick
went to Mussel Beach.
"Please teach us
how to surf,"
they asked Sandy.

"First, you need to keep your feet on the board," said Sandy.

"One, two, three.
Wheeee!"
called SpongeBob.

"Watch out, guys!"
yelled Sandy.
"The water is deep and
the waves are steep."

They gained more speed.
"I'm feeling wobbly, Patrick,"
yelled SpongeBob.
"Me, too!" called Patrick.

SpongeBob and Patrick
landed on the beach
in a heap.

"My knees are like jelly,"
said SpongeBob.
"Surfing is not easy,"
said Patrick.

"Hey, buddy, let's do it again!" said SpongeBob.

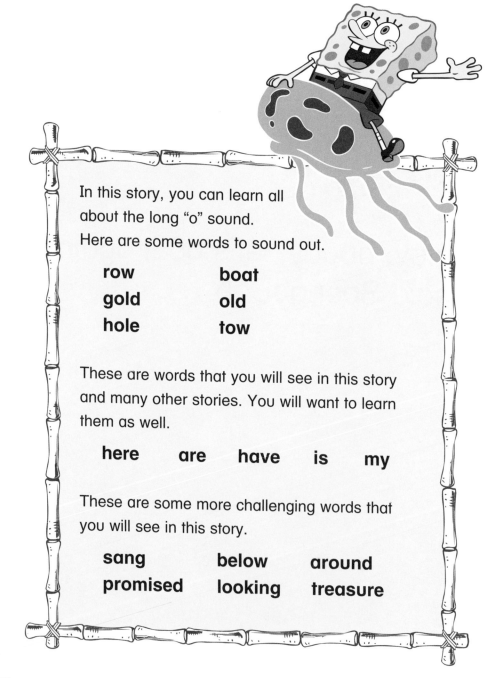

In this story, you can learn all about the long "o" sound.
Here are some words to sound out.

row	**boat**
gold	**old**
hole	**tow**

These are words that you will see in this story and many other stories. You will want to learn them as well.

here   **are**   **have**   **is**   **my**

These are some more challenging words that you will see in this story.

sang	**below**	**around**
promised	**looking**	**treasure**

BOAT TROUBLE

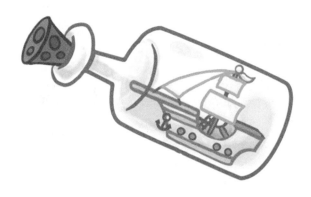

by Sonia Sander

"*Row, row, row your boat,*"
  sang SpongeBob.
"I can't wait to find
  the gold on this old map."

"Why do we need to
tow this big load?"
asked Patrick.
"Because we may need
these tools to find the gold,"
said SpongeBob.

"Hello, SpongeBob,"
said Mrs. Puff.
"Ahoy, Mrs. Puff,"
said SpongeBob.
"Our map shows you
have gold here. May we
look around?"

"Oh, I don't know,"
 said Mrs. Puff.
"You won't even
 know we are here,"
 promised SpongeBob.
"Okay," agreed Mrs. Puff.

"Why is there a hole
in my boat?"
cried Mrs. Puff.
"The gold is in this boat,"
said SpongeBob.
"No, it is not,"
said Mrs. Puff.

Mrs. Puff had an idea.
She put the golden
boat from her window
under a real boat.
"Why don't you try
looking below *this* boat?"
said Mrs. Puff.

"Wow!" said SpongeBob.
"We found golden treasure!"

"And now you must row away," said Mrs. Puff with a weary smile.

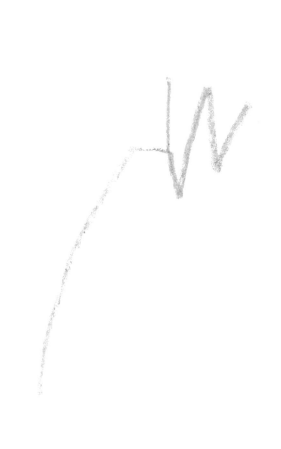